DEBT OF HONOR

TITAN BOOKS
LONDON

DC COMICS INC

JENETTE KAHN
President & Editor-in-Chief

DICK GIORDANO
VP-Editorial Director

ROBERT GREENBERGER
Editor

JIM CHADWICK
Director-Design Services

ROBBIN BROSTERMAN
Art Director

JOE ORLANDO
VP-Creative Director

PAUL LEVITZ
Executive VP & Publisher

BRUCE BRISTOW
VP-Sales & Marketing

PATRICK CALDON
VP & Controller

TERRI CUNNINGHAM
Director-Editorial Administration

CHANTAL D'AULNIS
VP-Business Affairs

LILLIAN LASERSON
VP-Legal Affairs

BOB ROZAKIS
Production Director

STAR TREK: DEBT OF HONOR published by Titan Books Ltd, 19 Valentine Place, London SE1 8QH, by arrangement with DC Comics Inc., 1325 Avenue of the Americas, New York, NY 10019 Authorized User under exclusive license from Paramount Pictures Corporation. STAR TREK art and text material Copyright © 1992 Paramount Pictures Corporation. All Righrts Reserved. STAR TREK is a Registered Trademark of Paramount Pictures Corporation. All other material Copyright © 1991 DC Comics Inc. All Rights Reserved. The story, characters and incidents mentioned in this book are entirely fictional. Printed in Canada. 10 9 8 7 6 5 4 3 2 1

The creators wish to acknowledge the contributions of all those who produced Star Trek *over the years, in all its myriad forms, for the inspiration that helped create this story. Adam and Karl wish to thank O.T. Wade, Brian J. Stelfreeze, Christina M. Abbott-Story, Joe Phillips, Andrew Morgan, Bryan Glass, and Michael Oeming. Gordon Purcell should also be thanked for his layout assistance. Thanks to Nick Napolitano for exacting paste-up. Finally, a thank-you to Carla Mason at Paramount Pictures for her help and support.*

Jason Palmer - Cover Artist   Veronica Carlin - Publication Artist

STAR TREK®

DEBT OF HONOR

CHRISTOPHER S. CLAREMONT

WRITER

ADAM T. HUGHES & KARL C. STORY

ARTISTS

TOM J. McCRAW

COLORIST

ROBERT M. PINAHA

LETTERER

To Frank Hampton and "Dan Dare, Pilot of the Spaceways"—who first showed me the sense of wonder embodied in comics...

And Robert A. Heinlein—who did the same for me in prose...

And most of all, as always, to Beth... who keeps me honest.

—Chris

Bob—
The Great Bird truly responsible for the book you're holding.

—Adam

"CAPTAIN'S LOG, STARDATE 3131.3: FIRST OFFICER CHENOWYTH REPORTING--IT'S BEEN TWENTY-FOUR HOURS SINCE *FARRAGUT* WAS ATTACKED. SHIP'S STATUS HAS AT LAST BEEN STABILIZED AND THE MAIN ENGINES ARE BACK ON LINE, ALBEIT WITH BOTH IMPULSE AND WARP DRIVE AT OPERATIONAL MINIMUMS. COMMENDATIONS ARE IN ORDER FOR ENGINEER-THIRD *DIANE MORWOOD* AND HER DAMAGE CONTROL CREW.

"THAT'S THE GOOD NEWS. WE'VE NO IDEA WHAT FORCE OR WEAPON STRUCK US. SENSORS PROVIDED NO ADVANCE WARNING AND SHIELDS NO DEFENSE. DAMAGE TO INTERNAL DATA STORAGE NETWORKS HAVE LIKEWISE LEFT US WITH NO RECORD OF THE INCURSION...

"...SAVE THE EVIDENCE OF OUR OWN EYES.

"A NEWLY-COMMISSIONED *CONSTITUTION* CLASS STARSHIP, REDUCED IN ALMOST LESS TIME THAN IT TAKES TO TELL...

"...TO A BARELY FUNCTIONAL DERELICT, LITTLE BETTER THAN A HULK.

"WITH FULLY A THIRD OF HER CREW--INCLUDING *CAPTAIN GARROVIK*--SLAIN.

"OUR LIFE SCIENCE AND MEDICAL DEPARTMENTS WERE DECIMATED, SO WE'VE NO WAY OF DETERMINING OURSELVES WHAT KILLED THEM, ALTHOUGH NOTES AND RANDOM TRICORDER TELEMETRY INDICATES SOME CRUCIAL DISRUPTION IN BLOOD CHEMISTRY.

"I'M NOT A DOCTOR, THOUGH, I HAVEN'T A CLUE.

"I'M A SHIP DRIVER WHOSE COMMAND IS ADRIFT IN SUCH PAINFULLY CLOSE PROXIMITY TO THE *ROMULAN NEUTRAL ZONE* WE DARE NOT EVEN RISK A SUBSPACE CALL FOR HELP.

"FOR ALL I KNOW, THE ROMULANS MAY ALREADY BE AWARE OF OUR PREDICAMENT...

"...AND ARE RUSHING TO OUR 'RESCUE.'

10

"TURBOLIFTS SPOIL YOU. NOTHING LIKE HAVING TO CLAMBER UP AND DOWN "JEFFRIES TUBES" AND WALK FROM ONE END TO THE OTHER TO REMIND A BODY HOW BLESSED *BIG* THESE VESSELS ARE.

"I LOVE THIS SHIP. AND THE CREW. WHATEVER HAPPENS, I WON'T LET THE ROMULANS GET THEIR HANDS ON EITHER."

STATUS, MR. KIRK.

SYSTEM'S STILL *DOWN* ACROSS THE BOARD, COMMANDER. PRIMARY CORE ELEMENTS OF THE MAIN SENSOR ARRAY WERE BURNED OUT.

I'M REPLACING THEM AS *FAST* AS I CAN.

I UNDERSTAND, LIEUTENANT.

IT'D BE A ROUGH HAUL FOR A FULL COMPLEMENT OF FIELD TECHNICIANS--HELL, ACCORDING TO THE OPS MANUAL, THIS IS SUPPOSED TO BE A *DOCKYARD JOB*--AND VIRTUALLY *IMPOSSIBLE* FOR ONE MAN WORKING *ALONE*.

WHICH IS WHY I'VE BROUGHT YOU SOME *HELP*.

I AM T'CEL.

ONE OF OUR *PASSENGERS*, AN ELECTRONICS ENGINEER ASSIGNED TO ONE OF THE CONSTRUCTION TEAMS BUILDING THE NEW *WATCHTOWER* OUTPOST STATIONS WE'RE ESTABLISHING ALONG THE NEUTRAL ZONE.

IN A SENSE, YOU'RE BOTH *ORPHANED*. T'CEL'S TEAM WAS *WIPED OUT*, KIRK, AS WAS *YOUR* SENSOR CREW.

WITH ALL DUE RESPECT, SIR, I CAN MANAGE ON MY *OWN*.

I'M TOO TIRED TO BE *TACTFUL*, LIEUTENANT.

FARRAGUT CANNOT MANEUVER, ON WARP OR *IMPULSE*, WITHOUT NAVIGATIONAL SENSORS TO SCAN THE WAY AHEAD.

WE CAN'T DEFEND OURSELVES WITHOUT THOSE SAME SENSORS DETECTING INCOMING HOSTILES AND COORDINATING THE WEAPONRY SYSTEMS' *RESPONSE*.

THE *ROMULANS* MAY HAVE BEEN RESPONSIBLE FOR THE ATTACK ON *FARRAGUT*. EVEN IF THEY *WEREN'T*, WE PROVIDE TOO TEMPTING A PRIZE FOR THEM TO *PASS UP*.

EITHER WAY, THE LONGER WE *STAY*, THE GREATER THE *DANGER*...

...I WANT THIS SHIP *OPERATIONAL* AND I WANT US *OUT OF HERE*! AND IF THAT MEANS *SWALLOWING YOUR PRIDE* AND WORKING WITH A *VULCAN*, OR WITH THE *DEVIL* HIMSELF--

--YOU'LL *DO* IT, MISTER, AND BE GLAD.

I WANT A *PROGRESS REPORT* WITHIN THE HOUR!

AYE-AYE, SIR.

11

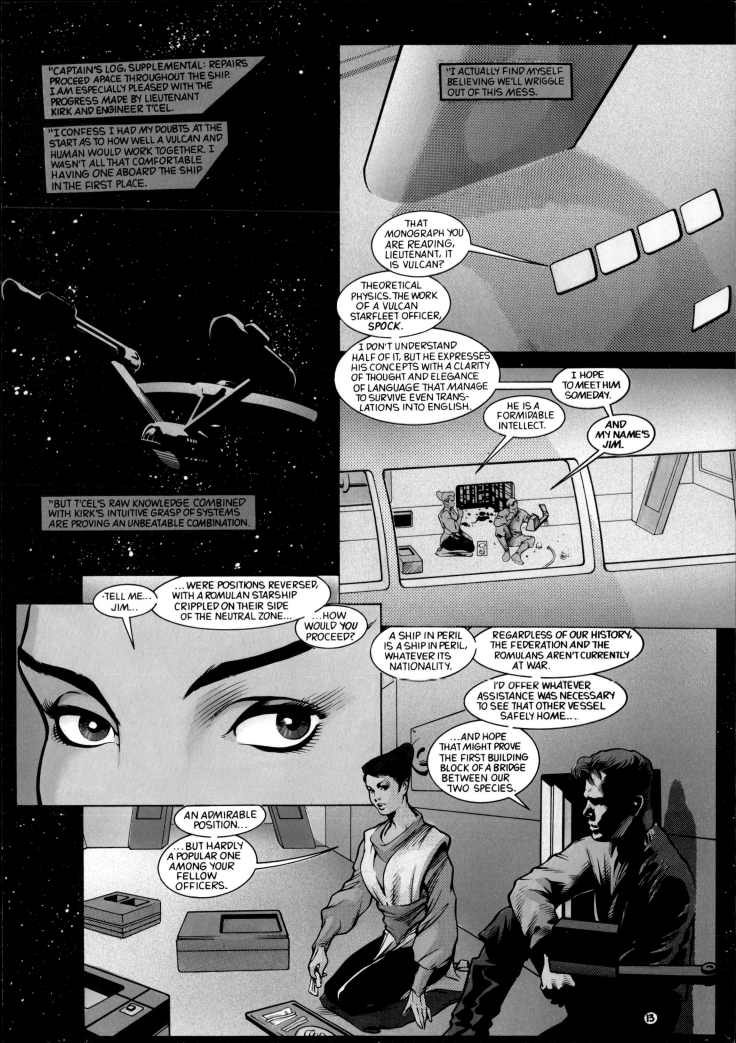

"CAPTAIN'S LOG, SUPPLEMENTAL: REPAIRS PROCEED APACE THROUGHOUT THE SHIP. I AM ESPECIALLY PLEASED WITH THE PROGRESS MADE BY LIEUTENANT KIRK AND ENGINEER T'CEL.

"I CONFESS I HAD MY DOUBTS AT THE START AS TO HOW WELL A VULCAN AND HUMAN WOULD WORK TOGETHER. I WASN'T ALL THAT COMFORTABLE HAVING ONE ABOARD THE SHIP IN THE FIRST PLACE.

"BUT T'CEL'S RAW KNOWLEDGE COMBINED WITH KIRK'S INTUITIVE GRASP OF SYSTEMS ARE PROVING AN UNBEATABLE COMBINATION.

"I ACTUALLY FIND MYSELF BELIEVING WE'LL WRIGGLE OUT OF THIS MESS.

THAT MONOGRAPH YOU ARE READING, LIEUTENANT, IT IS VULCAN?

THEORETICAL PHYSICS. THE WORK OF A VULCAN STARFLEET OFFICER, SPOCK.

I DON'T UNDERSTAND HALF OF IT, BUT HE EXPRESSES HIS CONCEPTS WITH A CLARITY OF THOUGHT AND ELEGANCE OF LANGUAGE THAT MANAGE TO SURVIVE EVEN TRANS-LATIONS INTO ENGLISH.

HE IS A FORMIDABLE INTELLECT.

I HOPE TO MEET HIM SOMEDAY.

AND MY NAME'S JIM.

·TELL ME... JIM...

...WERE POSITIONS REVERSED, WITH A ROMULAN STARSHIP CRIPPLED ON THEIR SIDE OF THE NEUTRAL ZONE...

...HOW WOULD YOU PROCEED?

A SHIP IN PERIL IS A SHIP IN PERIL, WHATEVER ITS NATIONALITY.

REGARDLESS OF OUR HISTORY, THE FEDERATION AND THE ROMULANS AREN'T CURRENTLY AT WAR.

I'D OFFER WHATEVER ASSISTANCE WAS NECESSARY TO SEE THAT OTHER VESSEL SAFELY HOME...

...AND HOPE THAT MIGHT PROVE THE FIRST BUILDING BLOCK OF A BRIDGE BETWEEN OUR TWO SPECIES.

AN ADMIRABLE POSITION...

...BUT HARDLY A POPULAR ONE AMONG YOUR FELLOW OFFICERS.

IF ANY GOT THROUGH...

WE'LL CHECK FOR SURVIVORS.

MY PEOPLE FOUGHT...LIKE LIONS, KIRK! DID THE SHIP... AND STARFLEET...PROUD.

STOPPED THESE...BUG-UGLIES COLD!

REST EASY, AKANKE.

T'CEL, SUMMON A MEDIVAC TEAM--!

NO TIME...WORRY ABOUT ME!

CRITICAL CIRCUITRY ELEMENTS SMASHED.

THE PROBABILITY OF SIMPLE SURVIVAL IN SUCH AN ENDEAVOR, MUCH LESS SUCCESS, IS MINIMAL.

CAN'T EFFECT SEPARATION FROM THIS END.

SOMEONE...HAS TO GO BELOW...ENGAGE MANUAL RELEASE.

WHEN YOU PUT ON THE UNIFORM, T'CEL, YOU SWEAR AN OATH AND ACCEPT RESPONSIBILITIES.

STAY WITH MR. AKANKE.

NO SIGN OF A SECOND WAVE.

PROBABLY MOPPING UP THE LOWER DECKS, FIGURE THERE'S NO REASON TO RUSH THINGS.

SECONDARY HU

IF YOU VULCANS HAVE A DEITY...

...I WON'T OBJECT TO A PRAYER.

DON'T THINK ABOUT THE ODDS, MAN, JUST GET THE JOB DONE.

PRIMARY HULL

WAIT!

WORSHIP HAS ITS PLACE, BUT PRACTICAL EFFORT MIGHT PROVE OF MORE VALUE.

IN A COMBAT SITUATION, IS IT NOT BETTER TO HAVE A COMRADE TO WATCH YOUR BACK?

I THOUGHT I TOLD YOU--!

AND JUST HOW MUCH EXPERIENCE HAVE YOU HAD IN THAT CAPACITY?

APPROXIMATELY TWENTY-TWO MINUTES, SEVENTEEN SECONDS.

BUT I LEARN QUICKLY.

19

YOU...SAVED ME.

AT THE TIME...

...IT SEEMED THE MOST... *LOGICAL* COURSE OF ACTION.

SHE'S *LYING.*

MY GOD, SHE'S... *BEAUTIFUL.*

WHERE...?

ARE WE?

THE EXPLOSION THAT DESTROYED *FARRAGUT* ESTABLISHED A FIELD IONIZATION EFFECT ACROSS THE SPECTRUM THAT INHIBITED THE POD'S COMMUNICATIONS SYSTEMS.

I DETERMINED THAT OUR BEST COURSE LAY TOWARDS ONE OF THE *WATCHTOWER* ASTEROIDS THE FEDERATION IS ESTABLISHING ALONG THE ROMULAN NEUTRAL ZONE.

AS I SURMISED, THIS SURFACE CONSTRUCTION SITE CONTAINS SUFFICIENT SUPPLIES TO TEND YOUR WOUNDS AND SUSTAIN OUR LIFE FUNCTIONS UNTIL THE ARRIVAL OF AID.

REGRETTABLY, MY ANALYSIS FAILED TO TAKE INTO CONSIDERATION THE FACT THAT THE *ROMULANS* THEMSELVES MIGHT CROSS THE NEUTRAL ZONE TO INVESTIGATE THIS INCIDENT.

THE SCANNERS HAVE DETECTED *A BIRD OF PREY* APPROACHING THIS OUTPOST. THEY WILL BE HERE SHORTLY.

THEY MUST NOT FIND YOU.

I HAVE REPROGRAMMED THE POD'S COMPUTERS TO SHOW MYSELF AS THE SOLE OCCUPANT. I WILL FLEE WITH IT, GIVING THEM AN EASY TARGET TO FOLLOW.

NO! MUST BE... ANOTHER WAY!

I AM PLACING YOU IN A *STASIS TUBE,* WHICH WILL KEEP YOU ALIVE WHILE SHIELDING YOU FROM ANY SENSOR PROBE.

WITH A LIVE PRISONER, THEY WON'T WASTE TIME GIVING THIS ASTEROID *MORE* THAN A CURSORY SCAN. THE STASIS TUBE SHOULD PROTECT YOU FROM THAT, AND ANY BOMBARDMENT.

I WANT THERE TO BE ANOTHER WAY, BUT I HAVE NOT YOUR GIFT FOR MIRACULOUS ESCAPES.

ALL I KNOW IS WHAT I SWORE BEFORE--AND SWEAR AGAIN, FOR AS LONG AS BREATH REMAINS TO ME--

--I SHALL NOT SEE YOU *DIE!*

LIVE LONG AND PROSPER, JIM KIRK...

...AND REMEMBER.

"PERSONAL LOG, LIEUTENANT JAMES T. KIRK: I STILL HEAR HER VOICE IN MY MIND, SEE HER FACE. NOT ALL THE TIME, BUT ALWAYS ETCHED AS CLEARLY AND VIVIDLY AS ACID ON CRYSTAL. SOMEHOW, T'CEL'S MADE HERSELF A PART OF ME.

"THERE'S SO MUCH WE DON'T KNOW ABOUT VULCAN, EVEN THOUGH THEY'RE OUR FRIENDS AND ALLIES. I SPENT MOST OF THE TRIP HOME, THE CONVALESCENCE THAT FOLLOWED, TRYING TO LEARN...

"...THE FINEST MONOGRAPHS ARE BY RESEARCHER AMANDA GRAYSON, BUT EVEN THERE I GET THE SENSE I'M BARELY SCRATCHING THE SURFACE.

"THE DAY I'M RELEASED FROM REHAB, I RECEIVE A SUMMONS FROM STARFLEET COMMAND."

BLAST IT, MS. FLEISHER, I'M A DOCTOR...

...NOT SOME DAMN PENCIL-PUSHING BUREAUCRAT!

IF YOU'LL PLEASE SIGN HERE, DOCTOR McCOY...

"THE OFFICE OF THE CHIEF OF STARFLEET OPERATIONS...

"...I WONDER IF THEY'RE GOING TO BYPASS THE FORMALITY OF A COURT OF INQUIRY ABOUT CAPTAIN GARROVIK'S DEATH...

"...AND SIMPLY ASK FOR MY RESIGNATION?

"I WONDER, CAN I LIVE THE REST OF MY LIFE IN IOWA AFTER I'VE SAILED THE STARS...?"

I READ YOUR REPORT, SON. I ALSO READ COMMANDER CHENOWYTH'S.

YOU WERE PRETTY HARD ON YOURSELF, HARDER, I SUSPECT, THAN CIRCUMSTANCES WARRANT.

SIR--!

FARRAGUT'S FIRST OFFICER, ON THE OTHER HAND, CONSIDERS YOU RESPONSIBLE FOR SAVING THE SHIP, AT WHAT WAS VERY NEARLY THE COST OF YOUR OWN LIFE.

WELCOME, LIEUTENANT.

I HOPE THAT CANE'S MOSTLY FOR SHOW.

MOSTLY, SIR, THANK YOU FOR ASKING.

DOES ONE EXCUSE THE OTHER, SIR?

24

I CHOOSE, LIEUTENANT, TO BELIEVE ART CHENOWYTH'S ASSESSMENT TO BE MORE TRULY REPRESENTATIVE OF YOUR ESSENTIAL CHARACTER. CONSIDER IT THE PREROGATIVE OF EXPERIENCE. AND RANK.

YOU'RE TO BE COMMENDED FOR YOUR ACTIONS, JIM, NOT CONDEMNED. EVERYONE MAKES MISTAKES, SOMETIMES COSTLY ONES. IT'S THE RARE, VALUABLE FEW WHO TRANSCEND THEM. WHO LEARN. WHO MATURE. I'M BANKING YOU'RE ONE OF THEM.

I DIDN'T ACT ON MY OWN, ADMIRAL.

WHAT ABOUT T'CEL?

ROMULANS DENY HAVING HER, WHICH IS TO BE EXPECTED.

WE FOUND THE ESCAPE POD, SMASHED IN A COLLISION WITH A LOCAL ASTEROID. SUFFICIENT BIOLOGICAL REMAINS TO ESTABLISH THAT SOMEONE HAD BEEN ABOARD.

I OWE HER MY LIFE, ADMIRAL, TWICE OVER!

A PLAUSIBLE ARGUMENT CAN BE MADE THAT T'CEL WAS KILLED IN THE CRASH.

THE VULCANS ARE PURSUING THEIR OWN LINES OF INQUIRY BUT WITH SURPRISINGLY LITTLE ENTHUSIASM. SOME... AWKWARDNESS REGARDING HER FAMILY.

AND SHE MOST PROBABLY PAID FOR IT WITH HER OWN.

I'M SORRY. I WISH I HAD HAPPIER NEWS TO REPORT.

NO JOY FOR YOU THERE, EITHER, I'M AFRAID.

YOU SEEM TO BE THE ONLY SURVIVOR WHO ACTUALLY SAW THEM. FARRAGUT'S INTERNAL MONITORS WERE SO BADLY SCRAMBLED, THEIR DATA CACHES ARE WORSE THAN USELESS. THE ROMULANS PROFESS IGNORANCE ABOUT THESE CREATURES AS WELL.

ALL STARFLEET HAS TO GO ON IS THE TESTIMONY OF ONE JUNIOR OFFICER REGARDING A LIFE-FORM UNLIKE ANYTHING THAT'S BEEN ENCOUNTERED IN TWO CENTURIES OF SPACE EXPLORATION.

I DIDN'T MAKE IT UP, SIR.

AND THE CREATURES, SIR, WHAT ABOUT THEM?

NO ONE'S SAYING YOU DID, SON. BUT NO ONE ON MY SCIENTIFIC STAFF CAN ACCEPT AT FACE VALUE CREATURES YOU MAINTAIN CAPABLE OF RESISTING VIRTUALLY THE FULL DISINTEGRATING POWER OF A PHASER.

IN THE ABSENCE OF HARD EVIDENCE, THE CONSENSUS IS TO TAKE YOUR REPORT UNDER ADVISEMENT AND GIVE THAT PARTICULAR SECTOR A WIDE BERTH FROM NOW ON.

BEYOND THAT, WE'LL WAIT AND SEE.

EVERYTHING HE SAYS MAKES SENSE. ESPECIALLY IF AN IN-DEPTH INVESTIGATION RISKS STIRRING UP THE ROMULANS. BUT I FIND I CAN'T ACCEPT IT ANYMORE...

...THAN I CAN THAT T'CEL IS DEAD. I DON'T KNOW WHY, BUT I SOMEHOW SENSE I'D... KNOW IT IF SHE WAS.

I DON'T CARE WHAT COMMAND DECIDES. I'M NOT LETTING THIS REST.

THOSE CRITTERS HAVE A HOME, AND A PURPOSE. I'M GOING TO FIND OUT WHAT...

...AND MAKE SURE THEY NEVER ATTACK ANYONE AGAIN.

25

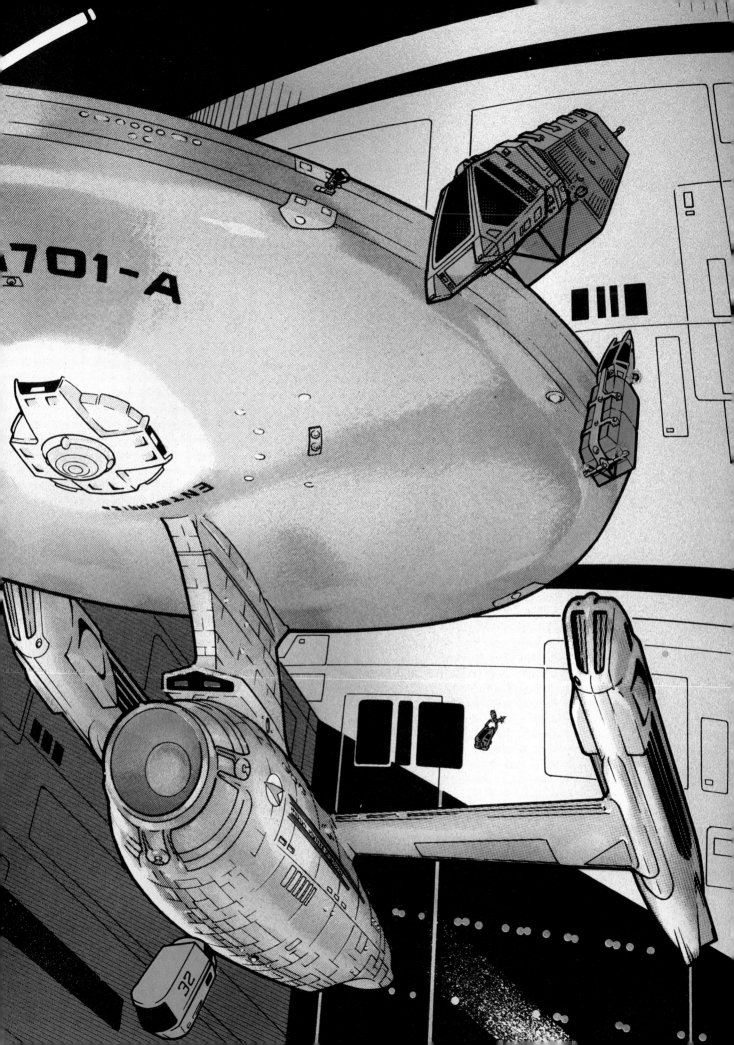

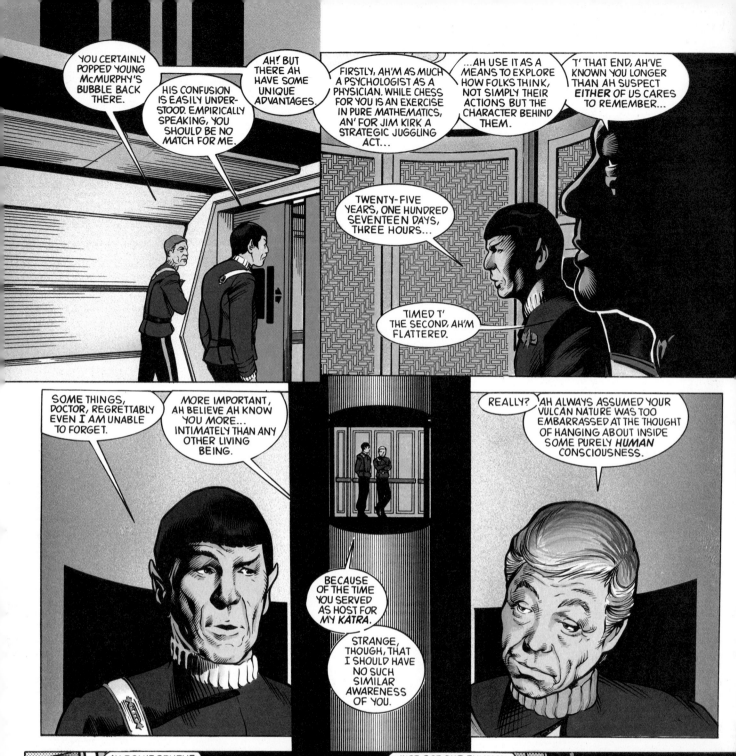

"SHE IS IN THE OFFICE, SIR, OF **COMMANDER JANICE RAND**...

"...STAFF SECRETARY TO THE *CHIEF OF STARFLEET PERSONNEL*."

ANYONE NOTICED YET, ABOUT ALL OUR PERSONNEL TRANSFERS?

IN A GREAT BIG BUREAUCRACY LIKE STARFLEET?

DEAR, YOU'D BE *AMAZED* AT WHAT CAN SLIP THROUGH THE CRACKS.

I'VE SCATTERED THE ORDERS AND AUTHORIZATIONS THROUGH ENOUGH NODES AND BACK-CHANNELS THERE'S VIRTUALLY NO WAY THE WHOLE PICTURE CAN BE PULLED TOGETHER.

ENTERPRISE WILL GET THE CREW YOU *REQUESTED*--THE BEST AND BRIGHTEST WHO'VE EVER *SERVED* IN STARFLEET--

--WITH NO ONE IN THE UPPER ECHELONS HAVING THE SLIGHTEST SUSPICION OF WHAT'S HAPPENING.

ALL PERFECTLY LEGAL. JUST NOT QUITE STRICTLY *BY-THE-BOOK*.

BUT THEN AGAIN, STARFLEET ENCOURAGES ITS PERSONNEL TO USE THEIR INITIATIVE.

YOU'RE ACTUALLY *ENJOYING* THIS!

MOST FUN I'VE HAD IN *AGES*!

JANICE, THIS *ISN'T A GAME*...

...ME, SCOTTY, SULU, CHEKOV, SPOCK, McCOY--WE'VE ALL BEEN THROUGH THE GRINDER, OUR CAREERS ARE PRETTY MUCH *FINISHED*, WE'VE NOTHING LEFT TO *LOSE*...

WHAT, YOU HAVE THE PATENT ON *LOYALTY*?

ENTERPRISE WAS MY FIRST ASSIGNMENT. THERE WERE TIMES THAT YEAR ABOARD I *WORSHIPPED* CAPTAIN KIRK. HELL, *HE'S* THE ONE WHO ENCOURAGED ME TO MAKE THE JUMP TO COMMISSIONED OFFICER!

I WOULDN'T BE DOING THIS--ANY MORE THAN *YOU* WOULD, UHURA--IF I DIDN'T THINK HE WAS *WORTH* IT. AND THE REST OF YOU AS WELL.

MY ONLY REGRET IS THAT I CAN'T COME ALONG FOR THE RIDE.

YOU'LL BE MISSED.

"...THAT'S SOMETHING ALTOGETHER DIFFERENT.

"CHIEF MEDICAL OFFICER'S LOG, U.S.S. ENTERPRISE, STARDATE 4203.5: BEEN PULLING OURSELVES BACK TOGETHER AFTER OUR ENCOUNTER WITH WHAT JIM CALLS THE 'DOOMSDAY DEVICE.' ME, AH THINK OF IT AS THE CORNUCOPIA FROM HELL.

"CHILLING, ACTUALLY, TO THINK HOW CLOSE WE CAME TO BECOMING ANOTHER OF ITS VICTIMS. COMMODORE MATTHEW DECKER, DESPERATE TO AVENGE THE LOSS OF HIS OWN CREW BY DESTROYING THE DEVICE, ALMOST ENDED UP DELIVERING US TO THE SAME FATE.

"IN THE END, THE SACRIFICE OF HIS OWN LIFE SHOWS US THE MEANS OF OUR SALVATION.

"MOMENTS LIKE THIS, AH WONDER WHAT SPOCK MUST THINK OF US, AS A SPECIES.

"FOR ALL DECKER'S EXPERIENCE AN' STRENGTH OF CHARACTER, HE WAS UNDONE BY A LOSS AN' A GUILT TOO TERRIBLE FOR HIM TO ENDURE. TO HAVE SENT HIS CREW TO WHAT HE THOUGHT WAS A PLACE OF REFUGE AN' THEN HAVE TO WITNESS THEM BEING SLAUGHTERED. TO BE THE SOLE SURVIVOR.

"WHAT PRICE OUR RATIONALITY IN THE FACE OF THAT KIND OF GRIEF?

CAPTAIN--

--I'M RECEIVING A TIGHT-BEAM S.O.S.

NO IDENTIFIER CODEX, BUT IT'S ADDRESSED TO YOU PERSONALLY AND ENCRYPTED IN A VULCAN SCIENCE ACADEMY MATRIX.

THERE'S A REFERENCE TO U.S.S. FARRAGUT. AND A TAG THAT INDICATES THE SITUATION IS CRITICALLY URGENT.

38

"MEDICAL LOG, SUPPLEMENTAL: IT WAS A MESSY, *BRUTAL* BUSINESS..."

"...CLEARING THAT COMPARTMENT AN' THE ACCESSWAY SO THAT THE UMBILICAL HOLDING US TO THE LARGER SHIP COULD BE SEVERED.

"WE LOST GOOD PEOPLE IN THAT FIGHT.

"WHATEVER REASONS JIM HAD FOR ORDERING US OVER HERE, AH HOPE THEY'RE WORTH IT.

"SOMETHIN' ABOUT HIM, WHEN HE LOOKS AT THESE BUG-UGLIES...

"...REMINDS ME UNCOMFORTABLY OF COMMODORE DECKER.

"'COURSE, NOW THE DANGER'S PAST...

"...IT TAKES NO EFFORT AT ALL FOR EVERYBODY T'REMEMBER...

"...HOW MUCH WE'RE ALL S'POSED T'*HATE* EACH OTHER.

"ALL OF A SUDDEN, JUST LIKE THAT, THINGS GOT VERY TENSE.

"AN' THEN..."

CREW OF THE *PHOENIX*, STAND YOURSELVES DOWN.

FOR AS LONG AS OUR *GUESTS* COMPORT OURSELVES AS SUCH, THEY WILL BE TREATED WITH THE COURTESY AND RESPECT DUE THEM.

YOU?!

!?!

"AH GRIPED ONCE THAT ALL MY OLD FRIENDS LOOK LIKE DOCTORS, WHILE JIM'S LOOK--WELL, A LOT LIKE THIS."

I'M *FLATTERED* YOU REMEMBER.

AND I SUSPECT YOU MADE SURE SOMEHOW I'D NEVER FORGET.

"AH WAS *JOKIN'*, O' COURSE.

"AH SHOULD'VE KNOWN BETTER.

"THE MAN REALLY *DOES* HAVE A KNACK FOR PULLIN' THE MOST BEAUTIFUL O' WOMEN OUT O' THE UNLIKELIEST O' HAYSTACKS. AND THIS ONE *TOPS THE LIST!*

42

"ENTERPRISE TO SAN FRANCISCO SPACEDOCK TRAFFIC CONTROL, PASSING OUTER MARKER, ALL SYSTEMS NOMINAL."

"ENTERPRISE, SAN FRANCISCO TRAFFIC, CLEARED FOR DEPARTURE VIA ROUTE VICTOR-ELEVEN TO LUNAR HOLDING STATION UNIFORM. MAINTAIN CURRENT VELOCITY."

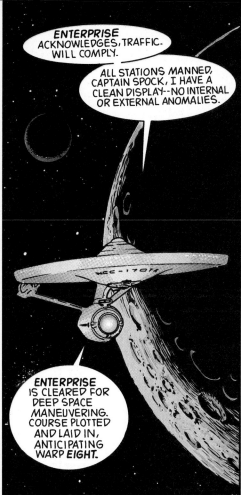

ENTERPRISE ACKNOWLEDGES, TRAFFIC. WILL COMPLY.

ALL STATIONS MANNED, CAPTAIN SPOCK, I HAVE A CLEAN DISPLAY--NO INTERNAL OR EXTERNAL ANOMALIES.

ENTERPRISE IS CLEARED FOR DEEP SPACE MANEUVERING. COURSE PLOTTED AND LAID IN, ANTICIPATING WARP EIGHT.

APPROACHING STATION UNIFORM.

RECEIVING A QUERY HAIL FROM THE DOCKING BUOY.

STATUS, PLEASE, MR. CHEKOV, OF OUR DRONE?

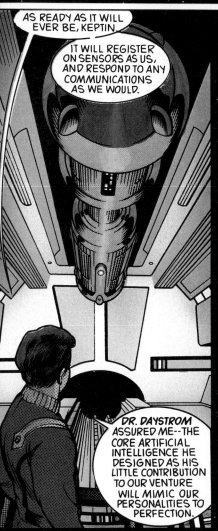

AS READY AS IT WILL EVER BE, KEPTIN.

IT WILL REGISTER ON SENSORS AS US, AND RESPOND TO ANY COMMUNICATIONS AS WE WOULD.

DR. DAYSTROM ASSURED ME--THE CORE ARTIFICIAL INTELLIGENCE HE DESIGNED AS HIS LITTLE CONTRIBUTION TO OUR VENTURE WILL MIMIC OUR PERSONALITIES TO PERFECTION.

AS FAR AS THE WORLD-- AND STARFLEET-- ARE CONCERNED, WE'LL BE RIGHT WHERE WE'RE SUPPOSED TO BE.

UNLESS SOMEONE COMES OUT FOR A VISIT.

EVERY STRATAGEM CARRIES ITS ELEMENT OF RISK, COMMANDER.

MR. SPOCK. ONCE WE DO THIS, WE'LL BE COMMITTED. THERE'LL BE NO TURNING BACK.

LAUNCH THE DRONE, MR. SULU.

"SCIENCE OFFICER'S LOG-- DESPITE THE CAPTAIN'S ADMONITION THAT COMMANDER SULU "INDULGE HIMSELF," OUR SHAKEDOWN CRUISE HAS TAKEN US IN FAIRLY SHORT ORDER BACK ALONG THE COURSE ESTABLISHED BY V'GER ON ITS APPROACH TO EARTH.

"OSTENSIBLY TO CATALOGUE AND EVALUATE THE DAMAGE CAUSED BY THAT ENTITY.

"BUT I SUSPECT AN ULTERIOR MOTIVE, A SUSPICION THAT IS FAST BECOMING A CERTAINTY WITH OUR APPROACH TO THE KLINGON FRONTIER.

"THERE IS A PREDATORY ASPECT TO THE CAPTAIN'S BEHAVIOR I HAVE NOT SEEN IN MANY YEARS. AN ASPECT OF HIMSELF THAT EMERGES WHEN, AS HE PUTS IT, HE "WALKS ON THE WILD SIDE." WHEN THE SHIP IS IN DANGER.

"WHEN THE EXPLORER GIVES WAY TO THE WARRIOR.

"HE IS HUNTING-- BUT WHO, OR WHAT, I DO NOT YET KNOW."

SENSORS IDENTIFY THE DEBRIS AS STRUCTURAL COMPONENTS OF A KLINGON DREADNOUGHT.

V'GER'S DOING, SPOCK?

DID IT TAKE OUT THIS SHIP, SAME AS IT DID THAT TRIO OF HEAVY CRUISERS?

UNLIKELY, CAPTAIN. IF YOU RECALL, THOSE TARGETS SUFFERED A COMPLETE MASS-TO-ENERGY TRANSMUTATION BEFORE BEING ABSORBED INTO V'GER'S DATA STORAGE NETWORK...

...THIS APPEARS TO BE THE RESIDUE OF A MORE CONVENTIONAL CONFRONTATION.

CAPTAIN, DEFLECTORS AND SHIELDS HAVE JUST RAISED.

I AM TRACKING A POTENTIAL HOSTILE ON AN APPROACH VECTOR, A ROMULAN BIRD OF PREY--

--FASCINATING.

I HAVE A POSITIVE IDENTIFICATION, COMMANDER T'CEL'S PHOENIX, RISEN ONCE MORE, IT SEEMS, FROM THE ASHES OF THE PAST. THEY ARE HAILING US, CAPTAIN.

OPEN A CHANNEL, UHURA.

IT'S BEEN A WHILE, T'CEL, YOU LOOK WELL.

OLDER AND SADDER, WITHOUT A DOUBT. I PRAY ALSO, SOMEWHAT WISER.

A STANDARD OXYGEN ENVIRONMENT EXISTS ABOARD THE KLINGON SHIP, JAMES.

I WOULD LIKE YOU AND YOUR SCIENCE OFFICER TO JOIN ME THERE.

ROMULAN INTELLIGENCE HAS BEEN PREDICTING FOR SOME WHILE A GROWING SCHISM BETWEEN THE TWO MAIN BRANCHES OF THE KLINGON RACE.

WITH THOSE POSSESSING A SMOOTH CRANIUM LOSING STATUS TO THEIR AGE-OLD RIVALS--WHO BOTH EMPIRE AND FEDERATION HAVE BEEN ENCOUNTERING MORE AND MORE FREQUENTLY OF LATE--WHOSE SKULL STRUCTURE IS MORE ARTICULATED.

KLINGONS DON'T LIKE FAILURE, EVEN WHEN IT ISN'T THEIR OWN FAULT.

IN THIS CASE, IT ISN'T SIMPLY THE LOSS OF SUCH A VESSEL, BUT THE FACT OF ITS VERY EXISTENCE.

IF I REPORT WHAT WE'VE FOUND HERE, JAMES, THE ROMULAN EMPIRE WOULD GO TO WAR, WITHOUT A MOMENT'S HESITATION AND WITH ALL OUR MIGHT AND FURY...

...AND WOULD NOT STOP UNTIL EVERY LAST KLINGON WAS ERADICATED. WE WOULD SEE IT AS THEIR SURVIVAL, AS A RACE, OR *OURS*, WITH NO MIDDLE GROUND.

THE FEDERATION, TOO, I SUSPECT. ALTHOUGH A TRIFLE MORE RELUCTANTLY.

THE KLINGONS AREN'T FOOLS, THEY HAD TO KNOW THAT. THEY MUST HAVE GAMBLED THAT THE FACT OF THE GUNSHIP'S EXISTENCE WOULD BE SUFFICIENT TO DETER ANY SUCH RESPONSE.

A *SWORD OF DAMOCLES* HANGING OVER ALL OUR HEADS, CAPABLE OF SNEAKING UP UNDETECTED ON ANY PLANET AND LITERALLY BLOWING IT OUT OF SPACE.

FOR ALL WE KNOW, THE DOOMSDAY DEVICE GAVE THEM THE IDEA.

WOULD'VE WORKED, TOO, IF THEY HADN'T BEEN ATTACKED BY THE CREATURES.

PERHAPS THAT'S WHERE V'GER CAME IN, BY SEVERING WHATEVER LINK THE INVADERS HAD WITH THEIR HOME BASE?

A VIABLE HYPOTHESIS.

DID YOU LEARN ANYTHING FROM FOLLOWING THEM, THAT LAST TIME?

I HAD TO BREAK OFF PURSUIT. MY OWN SPACECRAFT COULD NOT MATCH VELOCITIES AFTER THE CRUISER WENT TO *WARP SPEED*, AND ONCE THE "CRITTERS" ACTIVATED THE CRUISER'S CLOAK, WE LOST THE TRAIL COMPLETELY.

BUT THAT WAS NOT THE "*LAST*" SUCH ENCOUNTER, ANY MORE THAN THE *FARRAGUT* WAS THE FIRST.

I HAVE UNCOVERED ARCHIVAL EVIDENCE OF A SERIES OF *MYSTERIOUS* DISAPPEARANCES, STRIKING *ALL* THE STAR-FARING RACES INHABITING THIS SPIRAL ARM OF THE GALAXY, OCCURRING OVER THE BETTER PART OF THE PAST CENTURY.

EACH LOSS CONTIGUOUS WITH A MAJOR-- OFTEN CATACLYSMIC-- STELLAR EVENT, AND EACH INVOLVING QUANTUM LEAP, CUTTING-EDGE VEHICLES.

48

"BECAUSE OF THE TIME SCALE INVOLVED, AND THE FACT THAT NO RACE WAS EVER STRUCK TWICE, NO CONNECTION WAS EVER MADE BETWEEN THE DISAPPEARANCES."

"NO REASON WHY ANYONE SHOULD. MOST OF THE LOCAL RACES DIDN'T EVEN KNOW THE OTHERS EXISTED UNTIL FAIRLY RECENTLY."

"BESIDES, IT'S A BIG, BAD UNIVERSE. ACCIDENTS HAPPEN. I'LL BET EVERYONE ASSUMED THE SHIPS IN QUESTION VANISHED INTO THE CELESTIAL EQUIVALENT OF THE 'BERMUDA TRIANGLE!'"

BUT THE PATTERN EXISTS AND ITS MEANING'S CLEAR: SOME POWER IS CLANDESTINELY EVALUATING BOTH THE TERRITORY AND THE PLAYERS IN OUR GALACTIC NEIGHBORHOOD. DETERMINING OUR TECHNOLOGICAL AND MILITARY CAPABILITIES.

AND GIVEN THE NATURE OF THESE ENCOUNTERS, JAMES, WITH A CLEARLY HOSTILE INTENT.

I HAVE MADE MYSELF A PARIAH AMONG THE IMPERIAL HIGH COMMAND BY MY REPEATED ATTEMPTS TO ALERT THEM TO THE DANGER.

AROUND STARFLEET, THEY CALL THIS "KIRK'S FOLLY." THEY WANT EMPIRIC EVIDENCE.

WE'VE GOT IT HERE, CREATURES GALORE. BUT THE BODIES IN AND OF THEMSELVES MEAN NOTHING. WE'D HAVE TO SHOW THEM IN CONTEXT. WHICH MEANS REVEALING THE EXISTENCE OF THIS DREADNOUGHT. WHICH MEANS A THREE-WAY WAR.

THEY CAN ALWAYS BUILD ANOTHER.

DAMOCLES' SWORD CUTS BOTH WAYS, T'CEL. A TERROR WEAPON ONLY WORKS IF ONE PARTY POSSESSES IT.

WE'LL TAKE FULL-SPECTRUM SCHEMATICS OF THE GUN, A SET FOR ME. AND LET THE KLINGONS KNOW. PRESTO, ONE INSTANT BALANCE OF TERROR.

WOULD THAT ALL THREATS TO GALACTIC PEACE COULD BE DEALT WITH AS NEATLY.

THEY'LL BE BACK, THESE INVADERS.

WE CAN'T DO THIS ALONE.

WE MUST BE READY.

SEND ME WORD, JAMES, I WILL COME.

WHY DO YOU HAVE TO GO? T'CEL, THE FEDERATION WAS YOUR HOME!

NO. PHOENIX IS MY HOME. AS ENTERPRISE IS YOURS.

AND IF THE COST OF KEEPING HER-- OF STAYING TRUE TO MYSELF-- IS MUCH OF WHAT I ONCE HELD DEAR...

...SO BE IT.

CAPTAIN KIRK...

...YOU ASKED TO BE AWAKENED, SIR...

...UPON OUR APPROACH TO THE RENDEZVOUS.

THANK YOU, LIEUTENANT.

WATCHTOWER 13-- IN A SENSE, FOR ME, WHERE THIS ALL BEGAN.

APTLY NUMBERED, TOO. CONSTRUCTION WAS ABANDONED AFTER THE FARRAGUT INCIDENT. THIS SECTOR WAS CONSIDERED BAD LUCK.

BY THE ROMULANS AS WELL, WE LATER DISCOVERED. AND THE GORN, AND THE FIRST FEDERATION.

THEY ALL LOST SHIPS HERE, AT ONE TIME OR OTHER.

HOPEFULLY, THAT WILL END.

=SIGH=--

--AFTER ALL THESE YEARS WITH SPOCK, YOU'D THINK I'D HAVE LEARNED ABOUT COMPLIMENTING VULCANS!

THE SCANNER ALARM!

BY THE WAY, LIEUTENANT, WE APPEAR TO BE THE FIRST TO ARRIVE. MY CONGRATULATIONS ON A SUPERB FEAT OF PILOTAGE. I DOUBT EVEN COMMANDER SULU COULD HAVE DONE BETTER.

I AM MERELY DOING MY DUTY, SIR, AS A STARFLEET OFFICER...

...DEMONSTRATING COMPETENCE IN MY CHOSEN FIELD OF EXPERTISE.

THANK HEAVEN, SAVED BY THE BELL!

NCC-1701-A

WE'VE GOT COMPANY, SAAVIK!

THE FIRST OF OUR GUESTS IS ABOUT TO...

...ARRIVE.

NCC-1701-A
I TRUST, LIEUTENANT, YOU HAVE A VERY GOOD EXPLANATION FOR THIS.
NO, SIR.
WRONG ANSWER.
OPEN HAILING FREQUENCIES AND BRING US ABOARD.
51

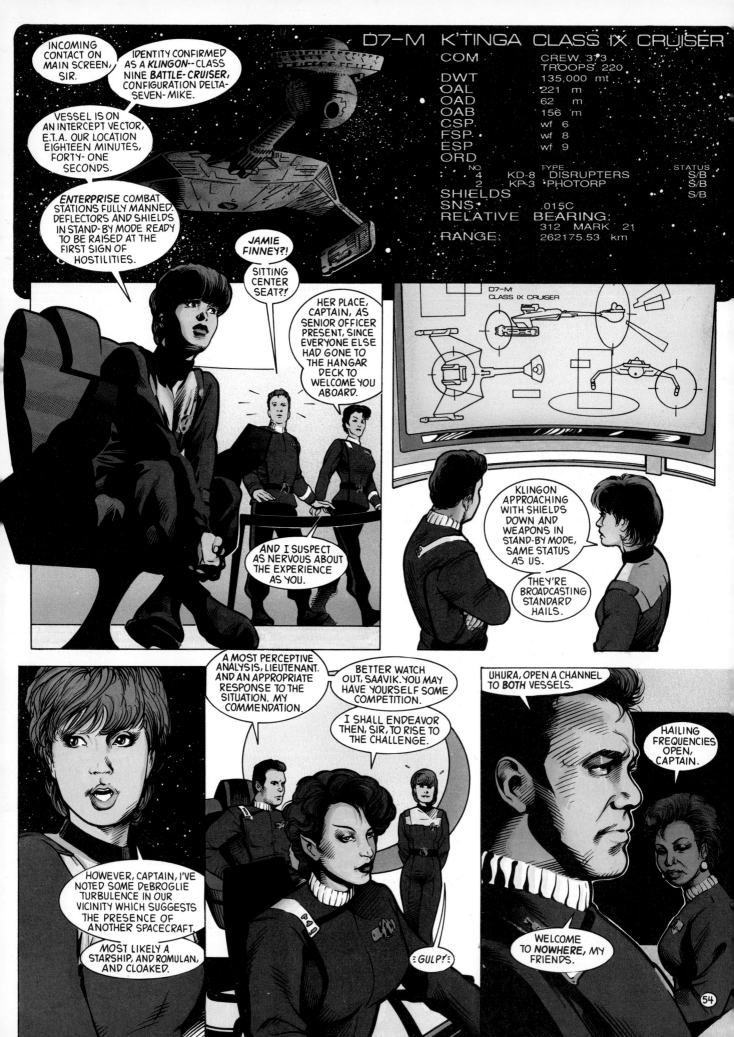

INCOMING CONTACT ON MAIN SCREEN, SIR.

IDENTITY CONFIRMED AS A KLINGON--CLASS NINE *BATTLE-CRUISER*, CONFIGURATION DELTA-SEVEN-MIKE.

VESSEL IS ON AN INTERCEPT VECTOR, E.T.A. OUR LOCATION EIGHTEEN MINUTES, FORTY-ONE SECONDS.

ENTERPRISE COMBAT STATIONS FULLY MANNED. DEFLECTORS AND SHIELDS IN STAND-BY MODE READY TO BE RAISED AT THE FIRST SIGN OF HOSTILITIES.

D7-M K'TINGA CLASS IX CRUISER

COM	CREW 373
---	TROOPS 220
DWT	135,000 mt
OAL	221 m
OAD	62 m
OAB	156 m
CSP	wf 6
FSP	wf 8
ESP	wf 9
ORD	

NO.		TYPE	STATUS
4	KD-8	DISRUPTERS	S/B
2	KP-3	PHOTORP	S/B

SHIELDS S/B
SNS .015C
RELATIVE BEARING: 312 MARK 21
RANGE: 262175.53 km

JAMIE FINNEY?!

SITTING CENTER SEAT?!

HER PLACE, CAPTAIN, AS SENIOR OFFICER PRESENT, SINCE EVERYONE ELSE HAD GONE TO THE HANGAR DECK TO WELCOME YOU ABOARD.

AND I SUSPECT AS NERVOUS ABOUT THE EXPERIENCE AS YOU.

D7-M CLASS IX CRUISER

KLINGON APPROACHING WITH SHIELDS DOWN AND WEAPONS IN STAND-BY MODE, SAME STATUS AS US.

THEY'RE BROADCASTING STANDARD HAILS.

A MOST PERCEPTIVE ANALYSIS, LIEUTENANT. AND AN APPROPRIATE RESPONSE TO THE SITUATION. MY COMMENDATION.

BETTER WATCH OUT, SAAVIK. YOU MAY HAVE YOURSELF SOME COMPETITION.

I SHALL ENDEAVOR THEN, SIR, TO RISE TO THE CHALLENGE.

HOWEVER, CAPTAIN, I'VE NOTED SOME DEBROGLIE TURBULENCE IN OUR VICINITY WHICH SUGGESTS THE PRESENCE OF ANOTHER SPACECRAFT.

MOST LIKELY A STARSHIP, AND ROMULAN, AND CLOAKED.

GULP!

UHURA, OPEN A CHANNEL TO *BOTH* VESSELS.

HAILING FREQUENCIES OPEN, CAPTAIN.

WELCOME TO *NOWHERE*, MY FRIENDS.

54

IT'S ALSO, YOUNG LIEUTENANTS, A MATTER OF COMBINING RESOURCES.

KLINGONS ARE FORMIDABLE SHOCK ASSAULT TROOPS. THE ROMULANS HAVE THEIR CLOAKING DEVICE, WHICH WILL HIDE THEM AND US FROM DETECTION.

AND CAPTAIN KIRK...?

WELL, SOMEBODY'S GOT TO BE THE GLUE THAT HOLDS THIS WHOLE CRAZY MESS TOGETHER.

THE PROBE THAT RECENTLY APPROACHED EARTH FITS THE PROFILE OF A MAJOR-LEAGUE STELLAR EVENT.

SINCE THEN, THANKS TO OUR BACK-CHANNEL EFFORTS, WE'VE KEPT THIS SECTOR FREE OF TRAFFIC, TO DENY THE INVADERS ANY POSSIBLE TARGETS SAVE OURSELVES.

THE PRESENCE OF ENTERPRISE ALTERS NOTHING OF THE PROPOSED PLAN.

TO MY SHIP AND MY CREW MUST GO THE HONOR OF BEING--TO USE THAT PHRASE OF YOURS, KIRK--THE STALKING HORSE. THE BAIT TO LURE OUR ENEMY INTO AN ATTACK.

THE LOSS OF THE DREAD-NOUGHT DURING THE V'GER ENCOUNTER CAUSED MY PEOPLE AN IRREDEEMABLE DISGRACE.

AS A CONSEQUENCE, OUR RIVAL KLINGONS GAINED ASCENDANCY IN THE HIGH COUNCIL...

...AND WE, AS A RACE, WERE DISCOMMODED.

BANISHED TO THE FARTHEST REACHES OF THE EMPIRE, STRIPPED OF THE RIGHT TO CALL OURSELVES KLINGON. STRIPPED OF OUR HONOR.

THE COUNCIL WILL NEVER RESCIND THAT ORDER, THE POLITICAL COST WOULD BE TOO GREAT.

BUT WHATEVER THEY SAY, WE MUST KNOW THE TRUTH. MY PEOPLE MUST LEARN THAT WE REMAIN TRUE TO OUR BIRTHRIGHT AND HERITAGE.

I UNDERSTAND ABOUT SUCH DEBTS OF HONOR, KOR.

THE PLACE IS YOURS.

56

"CAPTAIN'S LOG, SUPPLEMENTAL: WORK PROCEEDS APACE ON THE MATING OF *ENTERPRISE* TO T'CEL'S *PHOENIX*, ALBEIT WITH THE USUAL CHORUS, FROM BOTH ENGINEERING DEPARTMENTS, THAT THIS CAN'T BE DONE. NO ONE'S EVER TRIED LINKING TWO STARFLEET CRUISERS IN TANDEM, MUCH LESS ONE WITH A ROMULAN. BUT SUCH CLOSE PROXIMITY IS AN ABSOLUTE NECESSITY FOR US TO BE HIDDEN WITHIN THE FIELD OF THEIR *CLOAKING DEVICE*."

"THIS CONFIGURATION WILL SORELY TEST MR. SULU'S ABILITY AS HELMSMAN, ESPECIALLY IF WE SHIFT TO WARP SPEED. PRECISION MANEUVERING IS ESSENTIAL. IF OUR EVERY MOVE ISN'T PERFECTLY SYNCHRONIZED, THE RESULTS FOR BOTH SHIPS WILL BE CATASTROPHIC."

"IT DOESN'T HELP MATTERS THAT EVERY ELEMENT OF THE PROCESS IS ALMOST FUNDAMENTALLY ANTAGONISTIC.

"THEIR COMPUTERS WON'T TALK TO OURS, THEIR POWER SYSTEMS WORK ON DIFFERENT CYCLES. AND *NONE* OF THE PERSONNEL INVOLVED ARE COMFORTABLE WORKING TOGETHER.

"AND YET, JUST WHEN THE SITUATION SEEMS MOST HOPELESS, MR. SCOTT COMES UP WITH A SOLUTION. AFTER ALL THESE YEARS, I'M REMINDED OF JUST HOW *GOOD* HE TRULY IS."

"I FEEL SOMEWHAT... *ASHAMED* AT HOW MUCH, HOW OFTEN, I'VE TAKEN THAT INSPIRED BRILLIANCE FOR GRANTED."

CAPTAIN, THE ROMULAN CRUISER IS NOW INSIDE THE ARC OF FIRE OF OUR MAIN PHASERS.

COMMENT NOTED, MR. GARROVIK.

SIR, COMMANDER KOR WOULD WIN JUST AS MUCH HONOR FOR HIS PEOPLE BY THE *CAPTURE* OF THE *ENTERPRISE*-- AND YOU.

YOU SUSPECT TREACHERY?

I'D BE DERELICT IN MY DUTY IF I DIDN'T AT LEAST ACKNOWLEDGE THE POSSIBILITY.

BUT *FRIENDS*, AS WELL. WHOSE CHARACTER I'VE COME TO *RESPECT*.

YOU'VE MADE A LOT OF ENEMIES, JIM.

AND WHOSE WORD I *TRUST*.

THAT MAY WELL APPLY TO KOR AND T'CEL-- BUT WHAT ABOUT THEIR CREWS?

WE'RE ALL IN THIS TOGETHER, COMMODORE. *ENTERPRISE* NEEDS THE CLOAK: *PHOENIX* NEEDS OUR GREATER POWER TO SUSTAIN IT.

RISKY OR NOT, WE HAVE TO ASSUME THE BEST OF ALL INVOLVED...

...OR WE'RE *BEATEN* BEFORE WE START.

59

"CAPTAIN'S LOG, SUPPLEMENTAL..."

BIP!

"...OUR PREPARATIONS ARE COMPLETE. YET AGAIN, WE'VE ARRIVED AT A MOMENT OF TRUTH, AS I ACTIVATE THE CLOAK."

"MY COMMENDATIONS TO BOTH MR. SCOTT AND HIS ROMULAN COUNTERPART.

"I ONLY HOPE, FOR ALL OUR SAKES, THEY HAVE A FEW MORE MIRACLES TUCKED AWAY WHERE THAT ONE CAME FROM.

CHEKOV TO ENTERPRISE, YOU AND PHOENIX ARE FADING FROM ALL OPTICAL AND ELECTRONIC SENSORS.

CONGRATULATIONS, KEPTIN, THE CLOAK WORKS!

"WE'RE SURE TO NEED THEM BEFORE THIS CRUISE IS DONE."

HEY!

YOU! ROMULAN! WHADDYA THINK YOU'RE DOING DOWN HERE?! THIS IS A RESTRICTED AREA!

MY DUTY, ENSIGN, MONITORING THE LINKAGE BETWEEN PHOENIX AND ENTERPRISE.

YOU LOOK AT ME WHEN I TALK TO YOU, LADY!

AND YOU DON'T GO ANYWHERE ABOARD THIS SHIP WITHOUT AN ESCORT!

MR. RASCHE! THERE SOME KIND OF TROUBLE?

EVERYTHING'S UNDER CONTROL, MR. McMURPHY. NOTHING TO CONCERN YOU.

Oh, REALLY? DOESN'T SOUND LIKE THAT TO ME.

SUB-COMMANDER T'KIR IS LIAISON BETWEEN HER SHIP AND OURS. BOTH SHE AND COMMANDER T'CEL HAVE PLEDGED HER GOOD CONDUCT WITH THEIR WORD OF HONOR.

ROMULAN WORDS, SIR, ROMULAN HONOR. ONLY A FOOL TRUSTS EITHER.

THEN CAPTAIN KIRK IS A FOOL. AND SO AM I.

ONCE AGAIN, I AM IN YOUR DEBT.

LIKE I SAID, MY PLEASURE. ANYTIME.

61

OCH, THA' T'KIR'S A MARVEL, I'LL GRANT Y'. SHE'S GOT A RARE FEEL F'R STARSHIP SYSTEMS...

...I'M AMAZED WE GOT THIS JURY-RIG OPERATIONAL. I'LL BE BLESSED IF WE CAN KEEP IT RUNNING.

SO FAR, SO GOOD, MONTGOMERY.

AYE, TRUE ENOUGH, CHIP. BUT F'R HOW LONG?

CANNA SAY I MUCH LIKE HAVIN' ROMULANS CRAWLIN' ABOUT MY ENGINE ROOM, EITHER.

HAVE THEY GIVEN YOU CAUSE FOR CONCERN, MR. SCOTT?

NO, LASSIE, AN' THEY'D BETTER NOT, IF THEY KNOW WHAT'S GOOD F'R 'EM!

MAY I BE OF ASSISTANCE?

WE DO NOT ACKNOWLEDGE YOU, HALF-BLOOD.

YOU HAVE TURNED YOUR BACK ON ALL YOU WERE AND MIGHT HAVE BEEN, ON THE HERITAGE T'CEL EMBRACED.

HER HEART IS ROMULAN. MINE IS VULCAN.

TO YOUR ETERNAL SHAME!

THIS WAS THE ONE STORY ABOUT FARRAGUT I NEVER TOLD YOU, TOM, AFTER WE DESTROYED THE CLOUD CREATURE THAT KILLED YOUR FATHER.

NO NEED TO APOLOGIZE, JIM. I UNDERSTAND WHY YOU KEPT IT FROM ME.

WHAT D'YOU THINK WE'LL FIND OUT THERE?

WHATEVER IT IS, WE HAVE TO BE ITS EQUAL OR BETTER. THE STAKES ARE TOO HIGH, WE CAN'T AFFORD TO LOSE.

WHOEVER WOULD HAVE IMAGINED, MR. SPOCK--HUMANS, KLINGONS, ROMULANS...

...ALL SERVING TOGETHER, THANKS TO ONE MAN.

A REMARKABLE ACHIEVEMENT, COMMANDER.

WHOSE ULTIMATE RAMIFICATIONS WE CANNOT BEGIN TO GUESS.

THAT'S LONG-TERM, MR. SPOCK.

HOW ABOUT OUR IMMEDIATE FUTURE? THINK WE'LL FIND WHAT WE'RE LOOKING FOR?

GIVEN OUR CAPTAIN'S HISTORY, AND HIS PROPENSITY FOR SAILING INTO "HARM'S WAY"...

...I WOULD SAY THAT IS A VIRTUAL CERTAINTY.

"THE ASSAULT IS AS DEVASTATINGLY OVERWHELMING AS I REMEMBER.

"KOR LEAVES HIS INTERNAL VIDEO CHANNELS WIDE OPEN, ALLOWING OUR SENSORS TO MONITOR EVENTS ABOARD HIS SHIP.

"THE KLINGONS PUT UP A VALIANT FIGHT, AS WE DID ON THE *FARRAGUT*, A QUARTER-CENTURY AGO.

"AND TO MUCH THE SAME EFFECT.

"THE KEY QUESTION, HOWEVER, IS THE *CLOAKING DEVICE*. IS IT WORKING, ARE THE *CREATURES* AWARE OF US? I FIND MYSELF JUMPING AT THE SLIGHTEST HULL NOISE, HALF EXPECTING IT TO BE THE SOUND OF A HOSTILE PROJECTILE CRASHING INTO US. AND I WONDER, YET AGAIN, IF OUR PLAN IS TRULY AS GOOD AS WE THINK."

MR. SCOTT, WE'VE RECORDED MULTIPLE STRIKES ON THE *REVENGE*. KOR'S CREW IS TAKING CASUALTIES.

WHAT'S YOUR STATUS?

ALL TRANSPORTERS ON LINE, CAPTAIN, ALTHOUGH THE CLOAK'S MAKIN' IT DEVILISH DIFFICULT TO LOCK ONTO DR. McCOY'S TRANSPONDER TAGS.

RECALIBRATE THE INTEGRATOR MATRIX ALONG "D" CHANNEL, SARA, LASS, WHILE I TIGHTEN THE GAIN ON THE PRIMARY SIGNAL PATH.

"TIME IS OF THE ESSENCE, MR. SCOTT.

"I SUSPECT OUR KLINGON ALLIES COULD USE THE HAND..."

ENERGIZING, CAPTAIN. THE FIRST GROUP IS COMIN' ABOARD. BUT I'M AFRAID THEY DINNA LOOK TOO TERRIBLY PLEASED T' BE HERE.

WHAT HAVE YOU *DONE*, HUMAN?

HOW DARE YOU STEAL US AWAY FROM OUR COMRADES IN THE MIDST OF HONORABLE BATTLE?!

CAPTAIN'S ORDERS, LADDIE-- YOURS AN' MINE!

NOW CLEAR OFF THE PAD, THE LOT O' YOU, SO MS. TUCHINSKY AN' I CAN BRING OVER THE NEXT GROUP.

THESE CREATURES BURST THROUGH ARMOR AS EASILY AS *HORTAS* BURN THROUGH SOLID ROCK!

WATCH OUT, MR. CHEKOV!

VORGH!

AND USE VIRTUALLY A FULL POWER PACK FOR EACH KILL.

IT IS THE SAME WITH OUR KLINGON *DISRUPTORS.*

AS OUR TECHNOLOGY HAS IMPROVED, SO EVIDENTLY HAS THEIR ABILITY TO WITHSTAND IT.

SPACEEBA, CAPTAIN.

CHYORT VOZMEE! WHAT ARE THESE CREATURES *MADE* OF?

I NEED TO *RED-LINE* MY PHASER JUST TO MAKE AN IMPRESSION--!

NEECHEVO, TOVARISCH.

THE IRONY OF OUR PLIGHT IS, THE MORE OF MY CREW KIRK BEAMS AWAY TO SAFETY...

...THE MORE IMPERILED BECOME THOSE WHO REMAIN.

65

MR. SCOTT, THE INTERFERENCE IS GROWING ALL ACROSS THE TRANSPORT SPECTRUM!

IT'S AS I'VE BEEN SAYIN', CAPTAIN-- IF THIS KEEPS UP, WE'LL LOSE OUR TRANSPORTER LOCK ON THE KLINGONS.

WE DROP THE CLOAK, WE LOSE THE ADVANTAGE OF SURPRISE AND MAKE OURSELVES VULNERABLE TO ATTACK.

I'M SORRY, MR. SCOTT, YOU'LL HAVE TO MAKE DO AS BEST YOU CAN.

IF Y' DROP THE CLOAK-- JUST F'R A MINUTE-- WE CAN YANK OUT THE WHOLE KIT-AN' KABOODLE.

OTHERWISE, I CANNA GUARANTEE WE'LL GET EVERY- ONE.

EASY F'R YOU T'SAY, UP THERE ON THE BRIDGE-- EVEN IF YOU ARE RIGHT, BLAST YUIR EYES.

WHO'S LEFT, SARA?

COMMANDER CHEKOV, LIEUTENANT FINNEY, DOCTORS McCOY AND CHAPEL, CAPTAIN KOR AND HIS FIRST OFFICER.

WE'VE NO CHOICE. BRING 'EM OVER...

...AN' PRAY, LASSIE.

BUT THE SIGNAL'S AT MINIMUM TOLERANCE.

FOR A MOMENT THERE, SCOTTY...

IT WAS A NEAR THING, DOCTOR. Y' ALMOST DIDN'T MAKE IT.

WHAT ABOUT THE OTHERS? WE WERE ALL READY TO TRANSPORT!

THE OTHER SIGNALS WERE TOO WEAK. I HAD TO ABORT THE TRANSPORT, F'R FEAR O' THEM DISCORPORATING ALONG THE WAY.

WE'RE TOO FAR BELOW MINIMUMS T'MAKE ANOTHER TRY.

YOU DON'T KNOW THAT. AND IT'S A RISK I'M WILLING TO TAKE.

I'M IN NO MOOD FOR AN ARGUMENT, MR. SCOTT. DO AS I SAY--

--OR I'LL STUN YOU AND TRANSPORT MYSELF!

JAMIE, THAT'S SUICIDE!

SEND ME BACK, THEN. THEY'LL NEED THE HELP TO SURVIVE UNTIL YOU CAN MAKE ANOTHER ATTEMPT.

DON'T BE DAFT, GIRL. IT'S JUST AS UNSAFE BEAMING ONE WAY AS THE OTHER. AN' ONE MORE PHASER WON'T MAKE A DIFFERENCE.

I WON'T ABANDON THEM, MISTER. ENERGIZE-- NOW!

BONES, WHAT'S GOING ON--?!

THAT DAMNFOOL GIRL'S BEAMED HERSELF BACK ABOARD *REVENGE*, THAT'S WHAT!

JIM, WE'VE GOT TO DO SOMETHING. CHRISTINE CHAPEL AND CHEKOV ARE *TRAPPED* OVER THERE!

MUCH AS I WISH DIFFERENT, CAPTAIN, I DINNA SEE HOW.

AND KOR AS WELL!

SCOTTY?

WE LOST YOUNG FINNEY'S SIGNAL AS SOON AS SHE BEAMED OUT, AN' EVERYONE ELSE'S RIGHT AFTER.

I CANNA EVEN TELL YOU IF SHE SUCCESSFULLY MATERIALIZED ABOARD THE *REVENGE*, OR IF ANY OF THE OTHERS ARE STILL ALIVE.

WE COULD TIE THE PRIMARY SENSOR ARRAY INTO THE TRANSPORTER, CAPTAIN, USE ITS GREATER POWER TO PINPOINT THE BOARDING PARTY'S POSITION AND STATUS.

THE INTERFERENCE THAT AFFECTED THE TRANSPORTER IS SERIOUSLY INHIBITING OUR SCANNERS AND T-CEL'S.

TO GENERATE SUFFICIENT ENERGY TO OVERCOME THAT "STATIC" WOULD JEOPARDIZE THE EFFECTIVENESS OF THE CLOAK. IT WOULD VIRTUALLY GUARANTEE OUR DETECTION.

DAMN IT, JIM, D'YOU KNOW WHAT YOU'VE JUST DONE?!

CHEKOV'S YOUR *FRIEND* AS WELL AS ONE OF YOUR OFFICERS, NOT TO MENTION CHRISTINE--AND JAMIE'S YOUR *GODDAUGHTER*!

MAINTAIN "*SHADOW*" MODE, MR. SPOCK. PASSIVE SENSORS ONLY, WEAPONRY ACTIVE, TARGETING SYSTEMS ON STAND-BY.

WE'LL WAIT AND SEE WHAT THE CREATURES DO NEXT.

YOU'VE JUST SIGNED THEIR *DEATH WARRANTS*!

AGAIN, SPOCK, IF IT'S A CHOICE BETWEEN OUR LIVES AND THE SHIP...

...WE'RE EXPENDABLE.

MR. SULU, CARE TO JOIN US?

I WAS AFRAID, SIR, YOU'D NEVER ASK.

THE FOLLOWING PERSONNEL, REPORT TO THE HANGAR DECK IN FULL COMBAT GEAR: SUBCOMMANDER T'KIR AND HER TACTICAL FORCE...

...LIEUTENANT McMURPHY...

THIS IS IT.

DIE WITH HONOR, MY FRIEND.

NO OFFENSE, T'KIR, BUT LET'S HOPE IT DOESN'T COME TO THAT.

...AND DR. McCOY.

DAMN STRAIGHT AH'M COMIN', JIM!

"CAPTAIN'S LOG, SUPPLEMENTAL: THERE'S NO REAL NEED FOR THIS, REMOTE SENSOR MODULES COULD PROBABLY DO A FAR MORE COMPREHENSIVE JOB.

"BUT T'CEL AND I BOTH FEEL A NEED--AN IRRESISTIBLE DESIRE--TO LOOK THIS GORGON IN THE FACE.

"TO CONFRONT PERSONALLY THIS NIGHTMARE THAT'S HAUNTED OUR LIVES.

"I SUPPOSE THAT'S BEEN A HALLMARK OF MY CAREER IN STARFLEET--ESPECIALLY AS CAPTAIN OF THE ENTERPRISE--

"--TO CHARGE HEADLONG INTO THE DEADLIEST OF SITUATIONS...

"...SUPREMELY CONFIDENT OF MY ABILITY TO FIND A RESOLUTION...

"...AND A WINNING ONE, AT THAT."

74

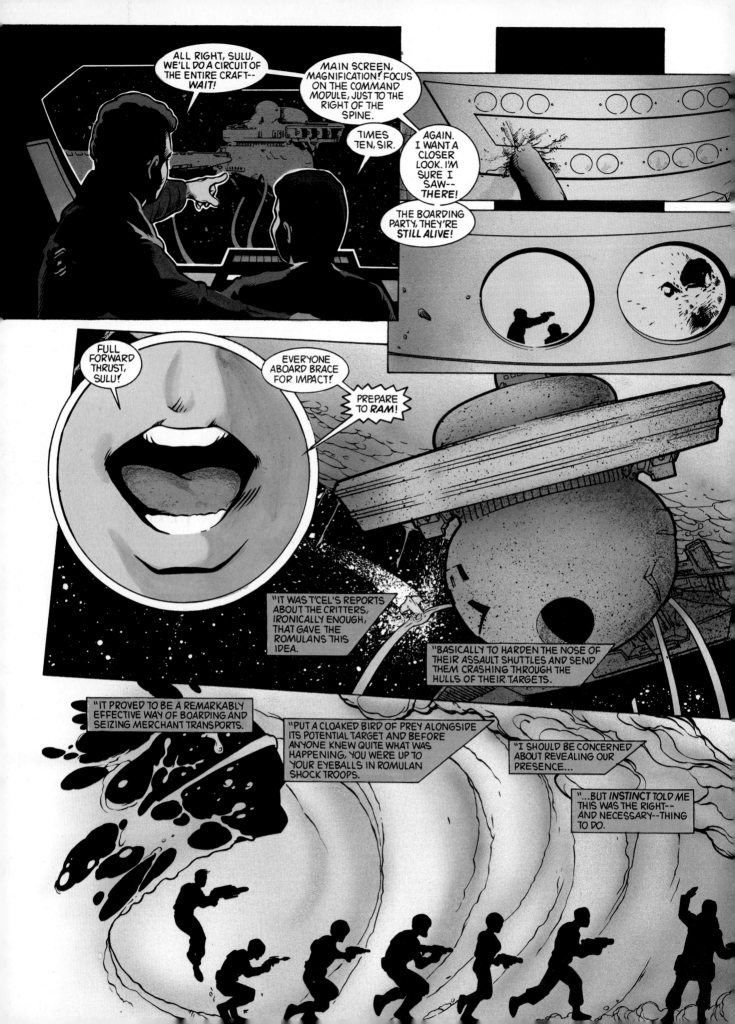

"CAPTAIN'S LOG, SUPPLEMENTAL: A POINT CAME WHILE THE *ENTERPRISE* WAS EXPLORING V'GER, THAT I LOST THE ABILITY TO COMPREHEND WHAT I WAS SEEING. THERE WAS SIMPLY TOO MUCH INPUT FOR MY BRAIN TO ASSIMILATE. THE WHOLE EXPERIENCE TOOK ON ASPECTS OF A DREAM, FLASHES OF IMAGERY RATHER THAN SPECIFIC POINTS OF FACTUAL OBSERVATION.

"WITH A DISTURBING SENSE OF *DÉJÀ VU*, I FIND MYSELF ONCE MORE WITH THAT FEELING AS I BEHOLD WHAT WE BELIEVE TO BE THE HEART OF OUR FOE'S SPACE-CRAFT.

"NOTHING IN MY EXPERIENCE-- PRECIOUS LITTLE IN MY *IMAGINATION*-- HAS PREPARED ME FOR THIS.

"THE CURVES, THE SHAPES, THE PATTERNS, THE DIMENSIONS-- ALL STRIKE ME AS... *WRONG.* NEVER HAVE I ENCOUNTERED ANYTHING SO TOTALLY AND OVERWHELMINGLY *ALIEN.*

"IT'S CLEAR FROM THEIR FACES THAT KOR AND T'CEL FEEL MUCH THE SAME."

FANCY MEETING YOU HERE, SPOCK.

IT IS MERELY, CAPTAIN, WHERE I MAY BE OF BEST USE IN THIS ENCOUNTER.

REPEATED COMMUNICATIONS WITH THE BOARDING PARTY WOULD HAVE EXPOSED THE *ENTERPRISE* TO AN UNACCEPTABLE RISK.

IN THIS WAY, WE-- AS *SCIENCE OFFICERS*-- GAIN ACCESS TO INVALUABLE RAW DATA TO ADD TO OUR STORE OF KNOWLEDGE, WHICH LIKEWISE ALONG WITH OUR ANALYSES AND DEDUCTIONS BECOMES AVAILABLE TO YOU FROM THE CACHES BROUGHT WITH US IN OUR TRICORDERS.

CAN'T FOOL ME, SAAVIK! I BET YOU GUYS JUST WANTED IN ON THE *FUN!*

THING IS, IF THIS IS THEIR "BRIDGE," WHERE'S THE CREW?

THEY MAY BE RIGHT BESIDE US, BUT BEYOND OUR ABILITY TO PERCEIVE THEM.

WE HAVE THUS FAR FOUND NOTHING RESEMBLING ANY CHARTED-- OR SPECULATED-- LIFE-FORM, CARBON-BASED OR OTHERWISE.

WE HAVE DETERMINED, CAPTAIN, THAT THIS VEHICLE TRAVELS BY TEARING RIFTS IN THE SPACE-TIME CONTINUUM WHICH ENABLE IT TO TRANSIT INSTANTLY FROM ONE PLACE TO ANOTHER.

HOWEVER, WHILE I HAVE DISCOVERED STAR CHARTS, MY TRI-CORDER HAS BEEN UNABLE TO IDENTIFY ANY OF THE CELESTIAL DISPLAYS.

I CAN ONLY CONCLUDE THAT THIS SPACECRAFT ORIGINATES SO FAR FROM EXPLORED SPACE THAT EVEN THE MILKY WAY GALAXY IS NOT EASILY NOTICEABLE.

A711-01

AAIIEEEEEE

A SCREAM!

JAMIE!
IT CAME FROM THIS SIDE GALLERY!

JAMIE-- LIEUTENANT FINNEY-- ARE YOU ALL RIGHT?!

GOOD LORD!

FASCINATING.

REDUNDANT AS IT SOUNDS...

...AH GOT A REAL BAD FEELIN' ABOUT THIS.

WATCH YOUR STEP. THAT SLOPE'S AS SLIPPERY AS IT IS STEEP.

I...I'M SORRY I CRIED OUT, SIR.

IT'S JUST... WHEN I SAW WHAT WAS INSIDE THESE COCOONS...

...I COULDN'T HELP MYSELF.

THEY'RE ALL DIFFERENT, BUT A LOT OF THEM ARE RECOGNIZABLE. SOME KLINGON, SOME ROMULAN, GORN OVER THERE, FIRST FEDERATION...

...I THOUGHT AT FIRST THEY MIGHT BE PRISONERS, HELD IN SOME KIND OF STASIS. BUT THINGS DIDN'T LOOK QUITE RIGHT.

AH THINK, AN' AH PRAY AH'M WRONG, BIO-LOGICAL CAPTIVES WERE DISASSEMBLED SAME AS THE SHIPS THEY CAME FROM.

TO SEE WHAT MAKES US TICK, AS WELL AS OUR ARTIFACTS.

POOR DEVILS.

SKRIK!

?

KRAKT!

JIM-- WE MAY HAVE OURSELVES A PROBLEM HERE!

80

"IT'S BARELY ENOUGH TO SAVE US.

"BUT IT IS *ENOUGH.*"

THE AFTER-EFFECTS WILL MAKE THIS SECTOR UNNAVIGABLE FOR THE BETTER PART OF A CENTURY.

AS NEAR AS YOUR MOTHER AND I WERE ABLE TO DETERMINE, THIS WAS THE CRITTERS' ONLY DOORWAY INTO OUR CELESTIAL NEIGHBORHOOD.

ATTACKS EITHER TOOK PLACE NEAR HERE OR THIS WAS WHERE THE HIJACKED VESSELS VANISHED.

SO, HOPEFULLY, WE'RE *RID* OF THEM. FOR AWHILE, ANYWAY. AND WE'VE ESTABLISHED A SOLID DATABASE TO ALLOW US TO PROPERLY PREPARE FOR OUR NEXT ENCOUNTER.

HOW'S YOUR WOUND?

HEALING QUITE NICELY, THANK YOU.

FOR ALL THAT HE LOVES TO PLAY THE CURMUDGEON...

...DR. McCOY IS A SUPERLATIVE PHYSICIAN.

86

MAY I ASK, CAPTAIN, WHY YOU DID NOT *JOIN* T'CEL?

YOU MAY ASK.

THAT'S A JOKE.

I KNOW.

FORGIVE MY IMPERTINENCE, BUT IT IS CLEARLY OBVIOUS...

...HOW MUCH YOU MEANT TO EACH OTHER.

OUT OF... *LOYALTY* TO ONE FRIEND, SPOCK--

--I *SACRIFICED* ANOTHER WHO WAS ALMOST AS DEAR TO ME, WHO'D SERVED ME AS LONG AND AS WELL.

STRANGE. AND SAD. YOU'D THINK-- I WISH, IN A WAY-- I WAS TALKING ABOUT MY *SON.*

BUT YOU MEAN THE *ENTERPRISE.*

SHE EARNED AN HONORABLE RETIREMENT. INSTEAD, I MADE HER A *ROGUE* SHIP, HUNTED AND DISGRACED. AND ULTIMATELY, I *KILLED* HER BY ACTIVATING THE *SELF-DESTRUCT* DURING THE GENESIS INCIDENT.

IF I FOLLOW T'CEL'S PATH, I'LL BE BLACKENING *THIS ENTERPRISE'S* NAME AND REPUTATION EVEN MORE SO, BEFORE SHE'S HAD HER CHANCE TO EARN ONE OF HER OWN.

THE SCALES HAVE TO BE BALANCED, YOU SEE, THE DEBT PAID.

IF A STARSHIP IS AN EMBODIMENT OF HER CREW AND CAPTAIN, THEN THEY LIKE-WISE ARE A REFLECTION OF THE SHIP, ENCOMPASSING BOTH HONOR AND SHAME.

ENTERPRISE WAS COMMISSIONED AS A VESSEL OF *STARFLEET.* IN STARFLEET'S SERVICE IS WHERE SHE HAS TO EARN HER PLACE. AND MY RESPONSIBILITY, MY... *PENANCE,* IS TO HELP HER DO IT.

MY MOTHER SAID YOU WERE *KINDRED* SOULS. I THINK I NOW UNDER-STAND WHY.

I HAVE A...*UNIQUE* HERITAGE, CAPTAIN. I HAVE SPENT MY LIFE LOOKING AT THE UNIVERSE FROM ONE PERSPECTIVE-- ALTHOUGH T'CEL TAUGHT ME TO BE AWARE OF OTHERS AND RESPECT THEM.

I WOULD LIKE TO REACH OUT TO THE *OTHER* SIDE OF MY BIRTH-RIGHT. TO BEHOLD THINGS FROM ANOTHER PERSPECTIVE, AND SEE HOW THAT WILL CHANGE ME.

A HARD CHOICE, T'KIR. AND A LONELY ROAD TO TRAVEL.

I AM AS POOR A *ROMULAN* AS MY MOTHER WAS A VULCAN.

I WOULD LIKE TO FIND OUT WHAT THAT MEANS.

IT WILL BE MY PRIDE, AND PRIVILEGE, TO HELP YOU LEARN.

THE PHRASE SHE USED TO CHIDE ME WAS TO CALL ME "PAINFULLY *HUMAN.*"

87

"T'CEL ISN'T DEAD-- SOMEHOW, UNSHAK- ABLY, I STILL KNOW THAT TO BE TRUE.

"AS I ALSO KNOW, GIVEN THE SLIGHTEST CHANCE, SHE'LL FIND A WAY TO RETURN. PROBABLY IN TRIUMPH. WHEN I TOLD THIS TO T'KIR, SHE SMILED AND SAID:

"MUCH THE SAME AS YOU."

"I LAUGHED.

"BUT SHE WAS RIGHT."

FINNEY, THERE IS *NO RISK*--TO FEDERATION OR EMPIRE.

SINCE THE *DISCOMMO- DATION* OF MY PEOPLE, WE HAVE BEEN ASSIGNED TO THE FARTHEST FRINGES OF THE EMPIRE. IT IS THE FUNCTIONAL EQUIVALENT OF *BANISHMENT.*

PHYSICALLY, OUR RACES ARE MUCH THE SAME. YOU COULD *EASILY* PASS FOR KLINGON, ALBEIT A SMALL ONE. AND YOU HAVE ALREADY PROVEN YOU POSSESS THE *COURAGE* OF A WARRIOR.

YOU HAVE MY *WORD,* NONE OF MY CREW WILL *BETRAY* YOU.

WHAT MORE PERFECT MEANS TO LEARN ABOUT US-- AND WE ABOUT YOU-- WITHOUT COMPROMISING THE SECURITY OF EITHER STATE?

KOR, YOU'RE *CRAZY!*

THAT'S *HARDLY A* PROPOSAL...

...WITH *STEEL!*

OCCASIONALLY, *LIEUTENANT,* A *TRUE* COMMANDER MUST THINK IN BROADER TERMS THAN THE SPECIFICS OF STATE POLICY, AND INTERPRET HIS OATH OF LOYALTY AND DUTY IN NEW, PERHAPS *REVOLU- TIONARY* WAYS.

...ANYONE WOULD EXPECT FROM A DECORATED KLINGON FLEET COMMANDER.

ON MY DECK, BOY, YOU HAD BEST BE PREPARED TO BACK SUCH *INSOLENCE...*

CONSIDER THIS MERELY AN OPPORTUNITY--

--LONG OVERDUE-- FOR OUR RACES TO GET TO KNOW ONE ANOTHER. AND PERHAPS TAKE THE FIRST FLEDGLING STEP TOWARDS THE FULFILLMENT...

IS THIS FOR REAL? AH SHOULD NEVER HAVE INTRODUCED THE MAN TO THE JOYS O' THE MINT JULEP.

THIS DOES SORT'A REMIND ME, THOUGH, OF THE "CORBOMITE MANEUVER"-- REMEMBER, SPOCK, LORD HOW *LONG* AGO WAS THAT--?

DON'T ANSWER THAT!

...OF THE *ORGANIAN* PROPHECY THAT, ONE DAY, FEDERATION AND EMPIRE WOULD BE BOTH ALLIES AND *FRIENDS.*

A PERCEPTIVE REMINISCENCE, DOCTOR. *BALOK,* COMMANDER OF THE FIRST FEDERATION'S FLAGSHIP, *FESARIUS* EXTENDED A SIMILAR INVITATION TO THEN- LIEUTENANT BAILEY, WITH POSITIVE RESULTS FOR ALL CONCERNED.

88

SPOCK'S RIGHT. UNFORTUNATELY, THE FIRST FEDERATION AREN'T KLINGONS.

YOU'LL BE FAR FROM HOME, JAMIE, AND YOU'LL BE *ALONE.*

I WON'T LIE, CAPTAIN. I'M SCARED STIFF BY THE IDEA.

BUT I ALSO CAN'T HELP THINKING OF THE *POSSIBILITIES.*

IF YOU *CAPTAINS* THINK I'M WORTHY...

...I'LL GIVE IT MY BEST SHOT.

IF THERE WAS THE SLIGHTEST DOUBT, FINNEY...

...I WOULD *NOT* HAVE ASKED.

HAIL THE CONQUERING HERO!

GIMME A *BREAK,* PAVEL, WILLYA? GEEZ-LOUEEZ!

GIVE THIS SOME THOUGHT, LASS. ARE Y' ABSOLUTELY *SURE?*

IN MY OPINION, IT'S A *MISTAKE.*

WE AND THE KLINGONS WILL *ALWAYS* BE ADVERSARIES.

WELCOME ABOARD THE *ENTERPRISE,* T'KIR.

ONE *OUTCAST* TO ANOTHER, EH, SAAVIK? THANKS, I APPRECIATE THAT.

CONGRATULATIONS, LIEUTENANT--IF THAT'S THE *WORD* TO USE.

WE SEEM TO HAVE CAST OURSELVES IN SIMILAR ROLES.

BEHOLD, KIRK, THE *NEXT* GENERATION-- OF STARFLEET, OF KLINGON, OF ROMULAN-- RUSHING HEADLONG TO EMBRACE A FUTURE...

...THE LIKE OF WHICH I NEVER EVEN *IMAGINED* UNTIL I MET YOU.

AND YET, *OLD* COMRADE, THERE'S SOME SATISFACTION IN KNOWING THAT, FOR ALL THE ROADS THEY FOLLOW, THE STRANGE AND WONDROUS DISCOVERIES THEY MAKE...

...THEIR PATH WAS BLAZED BY THE LIKES OF *KOR,* AND *T'CEL, McCOY* AND *SPOCK.*

AND *KIRK.*

THE FUTURE MAY WELL BE ONE OF INFINITE POTENTIAL...

...BUT *WE* MADE IT POSSIBLE.